The Contemporary Mouse

A FABLE FOR ART LOVERS

by Patricia Barnard

DRAWINGS BY CONSTANCE JEAN DOWLING

Photographs by Edward J. Moore, Staff Photographer, Museum of Fine Arts, Boston

Coward-McCann, Inc. *New York*

THIRD PRINTING

Library of Congress Catalog Card Number: 54-10139

MANUFACTURED IN THE UNITED STATES OF AMERICA

MICERINUS is an unusually cultured mouse. He should be, he has had unusual opportunities. His father had moved into the Boston Museum of Fine Arts only after carefully considering the resources of other cultural institutions, including Harvard University. A self-made mouse himself, he wanted his newborn son to have every possible advantage. As a start in the right direction, he decided to name him for the most important object in the Museum. Naturally, he assumed that this was the biggest object. And so—with a slight adjustment in spelling to make it more appropriate—Micerinus was named for a huge alabaster statue of the Egyptian Pharaoh Mycerinus*, who reigned some 2600 years before Christ.

Micerinus fulfilled his father's hopes from the beginning. At an age when less privileged mice were wasting their evenings playing hide-and-seek among dusty rafters Micerinus was searching for knowledge in the deserted marble halls of the Museum. As he learned his way through the miles of galleries, he discovered that the Museum was full of animals. Most of them were ancient compared to Micerinus, and many of them were ancient compared to anything at all, and they spoke of him rather condescendingly as "The Contemporary Mouse."

* Pronounced Mice ĕrēnus

ROMANESQUE BRONZE LION

Saxon (North German)
or Mosan, 12th century

One of the first animals he met was this little bronze lion who was made in the twelfth century in what is now the north of Germany and once supported something on his back—a candlestick perhaps.

The lion was indignant, incredulous and amused in rapid succession when Micerinus shattered his 800-year-old calm by running right under his nose.

"Good gracious," he exclaimed, "I do believe it's contemporary!"

And so Micerinus became The Contemporary Mouse right from the beginning.

PORCELAIN DOG

English, ca. 1751

Micerinus wasn't quite sure what contemporary meant, and he suspected that it wasn't altogether complimentary. He decided to ask the white porcelain dog, who was always friendly and democratic, in spite of being English, and in spite of the fact that he was made in one of England's earliest porcelain factories—about 1751.

"Contemporary," explained the dog, "means something that is going on now."

"Is that good?" asked Micerinus.

"We-ell . . . it could be worse," the dog assured him kindly. (He could remember how it felt to be contemporary.) "It's much better than being only fifty or a hundred years old. On the other hand, of course, it can't compare with being several centuries old. . . ."

STONE LION

Chinese, Tang Dynasty, late 7th century

"Or more than 1200 years old like me," interrupted the Chinese stone lion.

It was the Chinese lion who decided that Micerinus' education should be more systematic. He wore a bell around his neck which he rang when he wanted Micerinus to come for his lesson in ancient Chinese history.

"It was in the year 680 or 681 that I was placed on guard in the great Buddhist caves of Lung-mên. . . ."

"I beg your pardon, what men?"

"It's plain that you have no ear for languages," said the lion, "that's *mên,* not men. Lung-mên means Dragon Gateway, the rock cliffs overlooking the I River in Honan Province. Nearly a mile of Buddhist cave temples were cut into these cliffs and at the order of the Emperor the walls were carved with magnificent sculpture," the lion preened himself, "as, of course, any cultured person would know. *You* really don't know anything at all, do you?"

"Not very much, I'm afraid," said Micerinus.

BRONZE SHREW MOUSE

Egyptian, 600-400 B.C.

Micerinus felt less discouraged about being contemporary when he discovered the bronze shrew mouse who had been made in Egypt about four hundred to six hundred years before Christ. It gave him a sort of link with the past to refer casually to "my cousin from Ancient Egypt."

But the shrew only scolded him for claiming relationship with his betters, "I don't see any family resemblance at all. Just consider the slender refinement of my nose, for example, while yours—well frankly it's quite vulgarly blunt."

Micerinus lost his temper. "*Yours* is rather long and pointed, isn't it?"

"You don't really think it's *too* long, do you?"

The shrew looked so distressed that Micerinus forgave him at once, "Certainly not. It's very distinguished—and long noses indicate intellectuality you know."

"Thank you, *Cousin* Micerinus," said the shrew. "I can see that you're a mouse of most sensitive feeling—one of nature's noblemice in fact. . . . Now what would you like to know about Egyptian funerary customs? Perhaps you'd be interested to learn that I once decorated the coffin of a real shrew mouse deposited in a temple sanctuary as an offering. . . ."

BRONZE CAT ON PAPYRUS COLUMN

Egyptian, mid-4th century B.C

Bronze or not, a cat is still a cat. Micerinus stayed at a respectful distance when he called on this other neighbor from Ancient Egypt.

"Well, don't just stand there," said the cat, "What did you bring me?"

"I beg your pardon, I'd no idea it was your birthday. Many happy returns of the century. . . ."

"Never mind that," interrupted the cat. "As an animal sacred to the goddess Bastet, protectress of women, I never discuss age. Anyway I'm not talking about a *birthday* present. . . .

Don't you know that you're supposed to bring an offering when you pay your respects to a sacred personage?"

"Thank you for telling me," said Micerinus humbly. "I do have so much to learn. What would you like?"

The cat stroked her lean bronze stomach thoughtfully, "The Egyptians used to admire my athletic build, but I'm beginning to think that I'm a little *too* thin. . . ."

"Excuse me," said Micerinus, "I've just remembered a most pressing engagement."

MARBLE CAT, AMULET

Egyptian, 8th century, B.C.

Micerinus broke his resolution to have nothing more to do with cats when he met the tiny marble one worn as a charm by an Ethiopian queen of the eighth century before Christ. A cat smaller than a mouse! Micerinus squealed in delight.

"Well, don't be maudlin about it," said the cat coldly. "I may be small, but I'm monumental, as any *educated* creature could see. Monumentality, I trust you are aware, has nothing whatever to do with size."

"Of *course* not," said Micerinus hastily, resolving to consult the dictionary in the Museum Library as soon as possible, "I do beg your pardon. Now that I look closer I can see that you are a fine work of art. . . ."

"A precious treasure," agreed the cat, mollified, "In the Egyptian manner, of course."

Micerinus hurried home—by way of the Library—and practiced being monumental (enduring, imposing: *Webster*) for hours in front of a mirror.

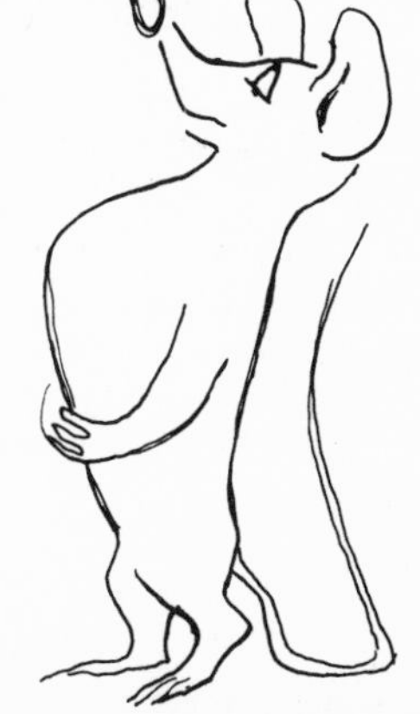

STONE LION

Indian, A.D. *300-600*

The next evening Micerinus practiced being monumental until he thought he had the hang of it. Then he set out to impress his friends. He was concentrating so hard on looking "enduring" and "imposing" that he forgot to look where he was going and bumped right into the stone lion from India. On one of his evenings in the Museum Library he'd read that Indian sculpture of the Gupta period (A.D. 300-600) was noteworthy for its "magnificent solidity." Now, as he rubbed the sore tip of his nose he was convinced.

"I do beg your pardon," he apologized. "I haven't quite learned to be monumental and observant at the same time. . . ."

"Monumental!" laughed the lion. "Impossible . . . you're much too realistic. In fact you look just like a real mouse. . . ."

"But I *am* a real mouse. . . ."

"That's just the trouble. . . . There's nothing left to the imagination. Now if you just *seemed* to be a mouse, you'd be much more artistic."

"Oh dear," sighed Micerinus, " 'To be or not to be'—that does seem to be the question."

POTTERY ELEPHANT

Persian, 12th century

"Are *you* realistic?" Micerinus asked the twelfth-century pottery elephant from Persia.

"Certainly not," said the elephant, "Almost everyone has a *white* elephant and some of the best people have *pink* elephants, but who ever heard of a turquoise-blue elephant!"

"But it's such a pretty color . . ." said Micerinus.

"That's reason enough," said the elephant. "And as far as that goes, do you think my *shape* is exactly like a real elephant's?"

"No-o, but it makes me *feel* how an elephant looks. . . ."

"Go to the head of the class," said the elephant, "or go to *my* head, if you like, and I'll give you a ride."

Micerinus was speechless with delight. He forgot all about being realistic and contemporary and just felt monumental as anything bowing to his friends from the top of an elephant's head.

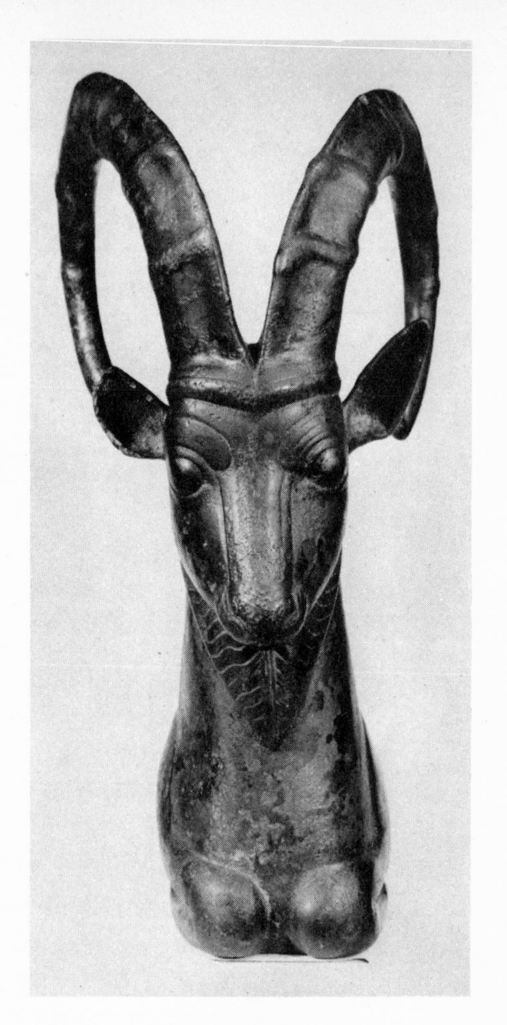

BRONZE IBEX, POSSIBLY AN ORNAMENT FOR THE ARM OF A THRONE CHAIR OR CHARIOT POLE

Persian, Achaemenian
5th-4th century B.C.

The Persian ibex was so noble and majestic in bearing that Micerinus could see at a glance that *he* was monumental. At first he was quite in awe of this new friend—after all as a symbol of rain and fertility the ibex had been a sort of god to the ancient Persians who had cast him in bronze four or five centuries before Christ.

The ibex' lessons in ancient history were most informative when Micerinus could get him to concentrate on the subject. Unfortunately he had one weakness—he not only liked to *talk* about the weather, he also liked to *do* something about it.

"Don't you think it's a bit stuffy in here?" he would ask hopefully.

"On the contrary, I find it quite comfortable. . . . Now you were saying that in ancient Persia. . . ."

"You're sure you wouldn't care for a little rain . . . just a refreshing shower? I'd be glad to arrange it. . . . It would be no trouble at all. . . . Just a sprinkle . . . ?"

And sometimes Micerinus would relent against his better judgment, "Oh very well, just a *very* light sprinkle. . . ." After all, it must be dull to be an unemployed god.

POTTERY HORSE

Chinese, Tang Dynasty, A.D. *618-907*

Most of the animals had learned to avoid the Chinese horse, who quite fancied herself as a lecturer on the fine arts. Micerinus innocently accepted the offer of a ride only to find that once in the saddle he was a captive audience.

"During the Tang dynasty in China—A.D. 618-907—it was customary to place figures reproducing the daily life of this world in tombs of the distinguished departed . . . images such as myself, for example . . . remarkably lifelike . . .

. . . handsome black glaze . . .

. . . bold modeling . . .

. . . Chinese funerary customs . . .

. . . superior craftmanship. . . ."

The mare talked on and on until poor Micerinus, for all his thirst for knowledge, began to wonder if it was possible to know *too much.* He decided to ask his gentle friend, the pottery cow from Delft.

POTTERY COW

Dutch, Delft, ca. 1775

"I dare say education for women is a fine thing," said the cow when Micerinus told her his troubles with the Chinese mare. "But in my day it was enough to be decorative—don't you think my flowers are becoming?"

The cow was the kindest of all the animals. She had no intellectual pretensions and she never tried to teach Micerinus anything. "You try too hard," she told him, "We can't all be monumental, and as for your being contemporary, you'll soon outgrow that."

"Will I really?" asked Micerinus, perking up, "I never thought of that."

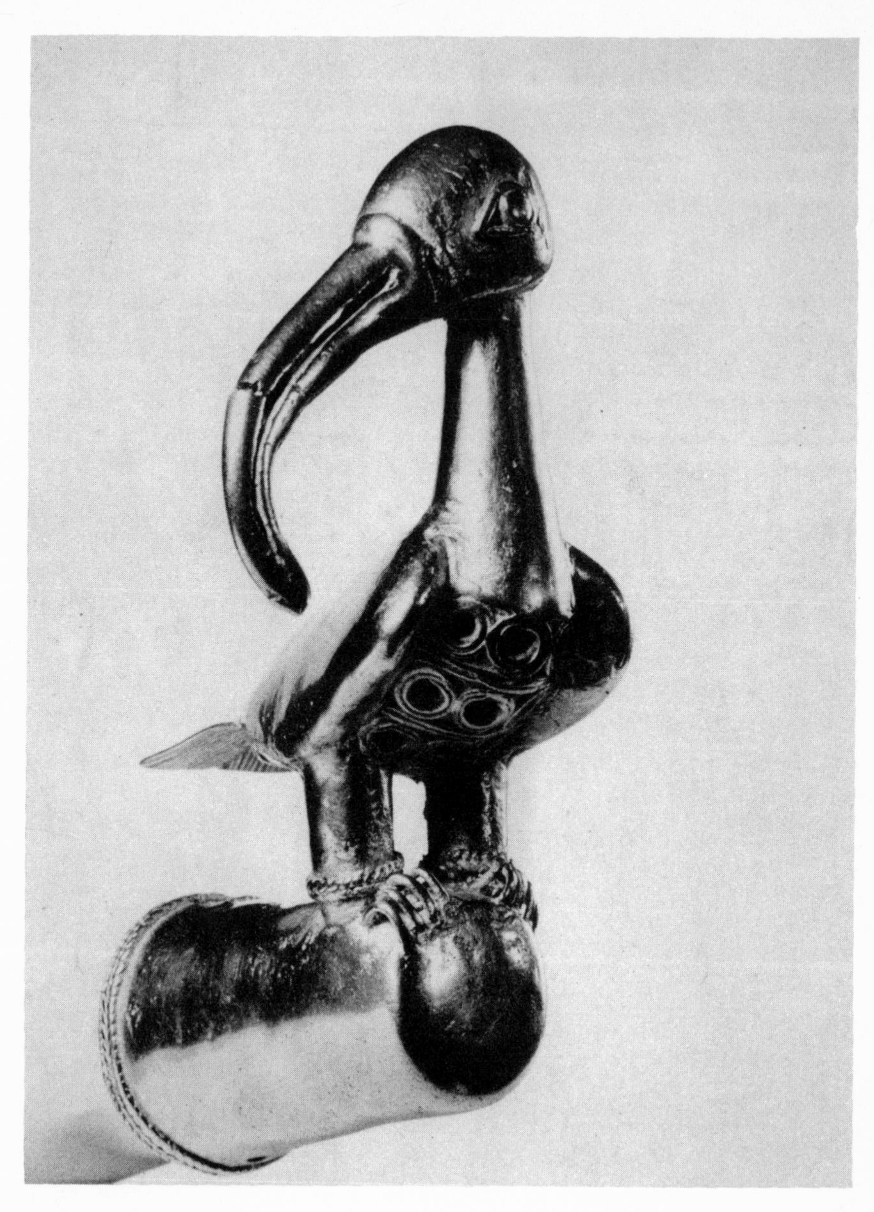

GOLD CORMORANT

Latin-American, pre-Columbian

Micerinus thought that he must have gone to sleep, for all at once he noticed that the sun was coming up. "Thank you so much, I must be going home now," he said politely to the cow.

"Nonsense," said the sun, "it's still the middle of the night."

Micerinus rubbed his eyes and looked again. The sun had a long hooked beak and it was speaking to the cow.

"You're spoiling the child," it said severely, "If he's ever going to learn anything at all, we must be firm. . . . Now Micerinus let's get on with your lessons, and stop staring as though you'd never seen a bird made of gold before."

"But I never have," said Micerinus.

"You see what I mean," said the cormorant (for that's what he was). "He doesn't know anything at all. Now please pay attention. Gold was freely used for many purposes in the South and Central America of pre-Columbian days. I myself once decorated a staff head. Sit down and write that fifty times."

TERRA-COTTA GOOSE AND GOSLINGS

Greek, 5th century B.C.

The Greek terra-cotta goose had been watching the lesson rather disapprovingly. "I think the cow is right," she said. "Children *should* be spoiled a little. Also, I'm not sure that too much knowledge is a good thing. Now look at my little ones, for instance. . . ."

TERRA-COTTA FOX

Greek, Tanagra, mid-5th century B.C.

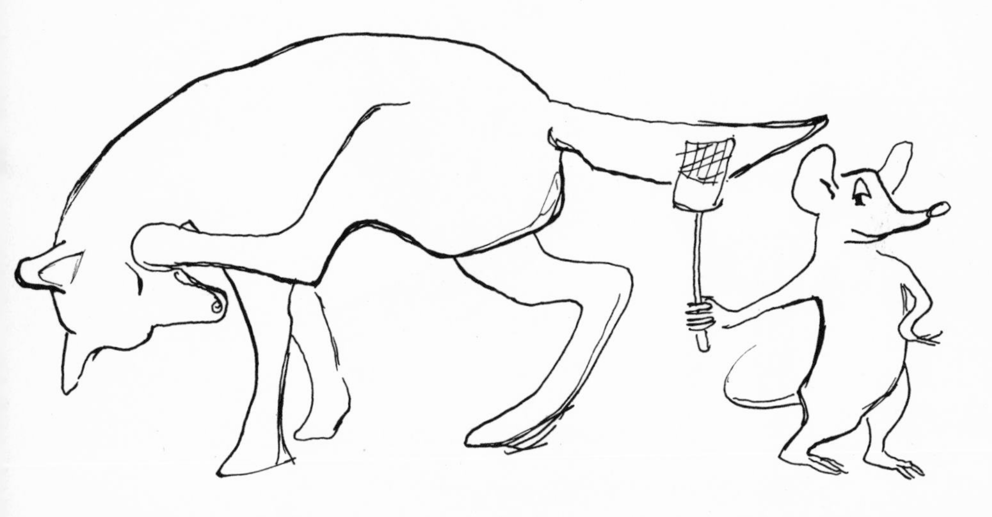

"Yes, just look at them," barked the terra-cotta fox. "After nearly twenty-five centuries they're still growing up to be geese."

"*You're* not setting a very good example in manners," remarked the golden cormorant.

"You'd be cross, too, if you'd been trying to get a flea out of your ear since the middle of the fifth century B. C.," snapped the fox.

"Run along, Micerinus," said the cormorant hastily, "You'd better go and talk to the Archaic Greek owl, who is exceptionally well educated. But first, have you made a note that the Greek fox and goose are figurines of the type used as offerings to the dead? The fox came from Tanagra and is most skillfully modeled. . . . You'd better write *that* fifty times too."

VASE IN THE FORM OF AN OWL

Archaic Greek, 6th century B.C.

"My time is precious," said the owl, "Let's get on with your education. I'm Archaic Greek and I date from the sixth century B. C.—but that's too dull for dialogue. You'd better put it in your footnote. . . ."

"What's a footnote?" asked Micerinus. He knew that the only way to learn is to ask questions.

"A footnote is what you put facts in, of course," snapped the owl. "What an ignoramus you are."

"Oh, of *course*," said Micerinus, and made his first footnote right away.

Footnote: The owl is a vase of the type used by athletes to carry the oil for anointing their bodies after exercise.

BRONZE DEER AND FAWN

Greek, 8th century B.C. *Geometric period*

"Good evening, how old are you?" Micerinus inquired politely when he met this charming little bronze deer and her fawn from Ancient Greece.* He had learned this Chinese form of greeting from his friend the lion from Lung-mên and had found it very useful in the Museum, where most of the creatures *like* to talk about their ages.

"I'm archaic, thank you, how old are you? . . . Oh, I *beg* your pardon, I forgot," stammered the deer. "You're contemporary of course. . . ."

Micerinus was getting sensitive about that word. He decided to postpone his visit to the deer and call upon the Egyptian pottery hippopotamus instead.

Footnote: Probably a votive offering, eighth century B. C., geometric period. Yes, that's really a bird perched on the deer's back.

POTTERY HIPPOPOTAMUS

Egyptian, pre-dynastic

"Good evening, how old are you?" Micerinus greeted the Egyptian hippopotamus, but this time it was the wrong thing to say. A large tear formed in the hippo's eye and rolled down his snout.

"I can't remember. I'm pre-dynastic. I may be as much as six thousand years old. . . . In fact I'm probably the oldest piece of sculpture in the round in the Western Hemisphere!"

"But that should make you *happy*," argued Micerinus, understandably confused. "Why you're older than the deer and the Chinese lion, and even the Ethiopian cat. . . ."

"I'm lonely. *Nobody's* as old as I am. . . ."

"I *am* sorry," Micerinus sympathized. Evidently this was almost as bad as being contemporary. He was considerably cheered.

TERRA-COTTA LEOPARD

Archaic Greek, 7th-6th century B.C.

Sooner or later, Micerinus made friends with almost all the animals in the Museum. Once they got used to his scuttling out of dark corners in such an outrageously realistic manner and startling them out of their ancient serenity, they were eager to help with his education. And if they were a bit sharp sometimes, it was only because, as the little Greek terra-cotta leopard of the seventh-sixth century B. C. explained, he had so many centuries of learning to catch up with.

"After all, dear," the leopard pointed out, "you *are* so *dreadfully* contemporary."

Micerinus understood and he was very grateful. Just to prove it, he wrote an exceptionally long footnote about his friend the leopard.

Footnote: Probably the handle for an Archaic Greek vase. Since the leopard was not native to Greece, this figure is evidence of the persistence of Oriental influence down to the fifth century.

BRONZE LION AND BOAR

Greek, early 5th century B.C.

But there were two creatures in the Museum with whom Micerinus never could make friends. The Greek boar and lion of the early fifth century B. C. were too busy quarreling to pay any attention to him—and that was too bad, because it was all a misunderstanding.

"You're a BOAR," roared the lion.

"You're LION," snarled the boar.

"And *you're* RIDICULOUS!" said Micerinus. "Even I can spell better than that. . . . If you'll just be quiet a minute I'll explain. . . ."

But they didn't even hear him, which was a pity because he did so admire the fine modeling of their bodies cast in solid bronze—such vitality . . . such *monumentality* . . . !

Footnote: Ornaments for the rim of a bronze vessel.

VASE IN THE FORM OF A MONKEY

Greek, Corinthian,
early 6th century B.C.

"It's no use asking *them* anything," warned the monkey from Corinth. "They've been snarling at each other that way for two thousand four hundred and thirty-four years—approximately. But I have lots of time and I'm much interested in higher education. Sit down, please. What would you like to know?"

Micerinus took a deep breath. "Please," he said, "Why is it bad to be realistic? How long does it take to get over being contemporary? And what can I do to make myself more monumental?"

"That's not at all the sort of question I had in mind," said the monkey. "But I should be glad to tell you about myself. I was made during the early sixth century before Christ. I am hollow inside, and like the owl, I used to carry oil for anointing the bodies of the famous athletes of my day. . . ."

"Thank you so much," said Micerinus politely, "But now would you mind telling me why it is bad to be . . ."

"Bad . . . Good . . . What big ideas for one so very small!" came a deep, rumbling voice, and all the animals were still.

Micerinus quaked. He tried to pretend he wasn't there.

"You may look at me, little mouse," boomed the voice with surprising gentleness.

Micerinus looked. At first all he could see was a great red stone paw, but as he raised his head, up and up, he finally found himself looking into the majestic face of the King of all the Museum creatures, the Greek lion of the sixth century B. C.

He was overcome with awe. How enduring . . . how imposing . . . how *monumental*. . . .

'ONE LION

Archaic Greek, 6th century B.C.

BRONZE WHIPPET

Katherine Lane, American, contemporary

"Whatever is the matter?" asked the whippet as Micerinus stumbled by him.

"I did so want to be monumental," said Micerinus. "And now I see that it's quite hopeless. . . . I'm just too realistic and too con—contemporary." He burst into tears.

"Oh come now, it's not as bad as that," said the whippet, "I'm contemporary too, you know. . . ."

"*What!*"

"I said I'm contemporary too. It's really not so bad, and anyway, as the cow told you, we'll outgrow it in a few hundred years."

"Do you think I'll *last* that long?" asked Micerinus.

"Well. . . . I must say you don't look very permanent in your present state. Now if you could get a sculptor to cast you in bronze like me. . . ."

Footnote: A whippet is a small, swift dog developed from a cross between a greyhound and a terrier. This one is the work of the American sculptor, Katherine Lane.

That day Micerinus dreamed that he sat for his portrait.

"Why of *course* . . . I'm *honored*," said the distinguished sculptor, "How kind of you to allow me. . . . Will you have bronze or marble?"

"Just make it MONUMENTAL, please," said Micerinus.